Contents

The bad goat
Focus on: oa, o_e as in b<u>oa</u>t, n<u>o</u>s<u>e</u> 3

When the cold wind blows
Focus on: o_e, ow as in n<u>o</u>s<u>e</u>, sh<u>ow</u> 8

Lost in the Queen's maze
Focus on: ow as in sh<u>ow</u> 16

Phonemes: ch, sh, th, wh, ph, a_e, ai, ay, e_e, ea, ee, y *as e*, i_e, ie, igh, y *as i,* **o_e, oa, ow**
'Tricky' words: my, can't, does, love, here, are, look, our, eyes

About this book

These short stories are designed to give children blending and reading practice. They are decodable, which means the words in them only include letter shapes and sounds that the children have learned. The stories gradually introduce 'tricky' words, building on the learning in the Red Series.

The progression links directly to the teaching order in the Letterland teaching range. Each story begins with a title page that provides important information for children and teachers.

Story title

Focus on: New spelling patterns introduced

New 'tricky' words: Common words with irregular spellings

Basic teaching tips:

- Encourage the sounding out of decodable words (and any decodable parts of 'tricky' words).
- Discuss the stories with the children to ensure comprehension and engagement.
- Encourage re-reading in pairs or individually to develop fluency and reading for meaning.

Red Series introduces the a-z letters and sounds and some 'tricky words'. On completion of this series, the following words remain tricky in part: a, the, she, oh, for, that, ok, they, says, her, this, to, said, of, what, you, was, want, come, sees, asks, do. These words are included in **Blue Series**.

The bad goat

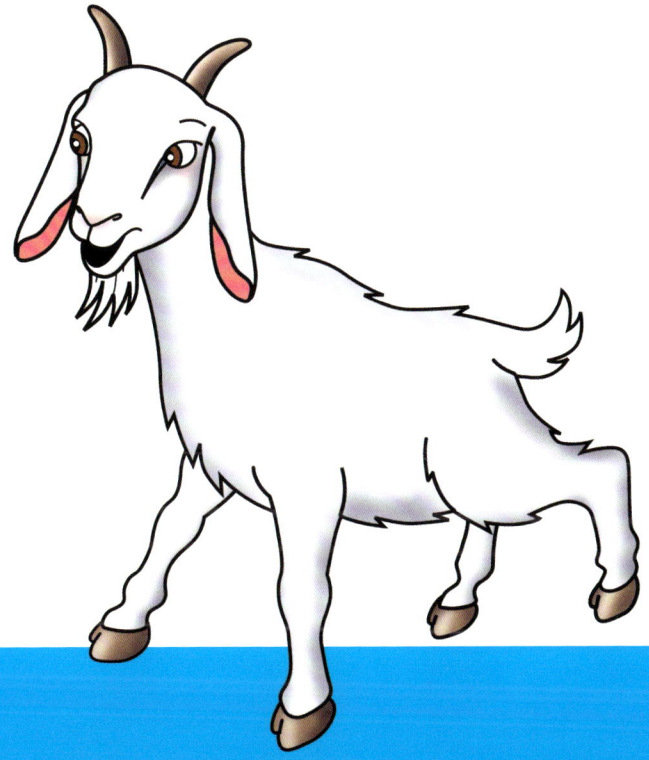

Focus on: oa as in <u>*boat*</u>

Fred loaded the truck with feed.
He fed oats to the foal.

The goat bleated at him, "Maaa!".

Fred cleaned the foal with soap. He used a hose and a big brush to get the foam off.

The goat bleated at him, "Maaa!".

The goat jumped up on the truck, and ate the oats!

"No, no!" Fred groaned. "Get off, you bad goat!"

The goat butted the bucket.

"Oh! No!" said Fred. "My coat is soaked!"

The goat bleated at him, "Maaa! Maaa!".

When the cold wind blows

Focus on: ow as in *sh<u>ow</u>*

When the cold wind blows and blows,

it stings your nose, and bites your toes.

Then you know, it's time for snow!

And when it snows and snows you say,

"Mum, can I go? Can I play?"

It's slow to plod in deep, deep snow,

but Rose and Tom are keen to go.

Thick clothes on and off you go.

All three of you with sleds in tow.

You get on a sled with best mate Rose.

A push from Tom - away you go!

Next you dig and roll in snow.

This is snow that you can throw!

And then it's night and time to go,

past homes with windows in a row,

back inside to mummy's hug.

It makes you feel so very snug!

Lost in the Queen's maze

Focus on: ow as in *show*

"Let's go to the Queen's maze!" said Jumping Jim.
"What's a maze?" asked Vicky.

"It's rows and rows of bushes that you can get lost in. It's fun." Jim explained.

"Hello," said the Queen. "Let me show you my maze. Go in here and find your way to the exit. Don't get lost!"

Jim and Vicky went in.

"Are there arrows to follow so we know which way to go?" asked Vicky.

"There are no arrows. We just have to find our way on our own," said Jim.

It was fun... for a bit. They went slowly but the rows began to look the same. "I don't know which way to go!" said Vicky.

Then the wind began to blow.
"Lightning! We need to get inside!"
Vicky tried to see which way to go but the maze was too high!

"I know, Jumping Jim! You can jump and show us the way!" said Vicky.

Jim jumped up. The maze was below him. "I can see!" said Jim.

Show them the way to the exit.

About this series

This series of 10 books accompanies the Letterland teaching range. Each book contains a selection of short stories. In total there are 32 engaging stories featuring the phonic elements listed below as well as some 'tricky' high-frequency words.

Book	Focus elements	As in the word...	Story titles
1	sh, ch, th, th, wh, ph	<u>ch</u>ip, <u>sh</u>op, <u>th</u>at, <u>th</u>ing	Check on the chicks Shep and me What is that thing?
2	a_e, ai, ay	m<u>a</u>k<u>e</u>, r<u>ai</u>n, s<u>ay</u>,	A safe place Kate bakes a cake Kane's tail!
3	e_e, ea, ee, y	th<u>e</u>s<u>e</u>, s<u>ea</u>, b<u>ee</u>, bab<u>y</u>	A trip to the sea Mr E's trees Happy!
4	i_e, ie, igh, y	l<u>i</u>k<u>e</u>, t<u>ie</u>, n<u>igh</u>t, m<u>y</u>	Ben rides his bike Cats at night What a mess!
5	o_e, oa, ow	h<u>o</u>m<u>e</u>, b<u>oa</u>t, sh<u>ow</u>	The bad goat When the cold wind blows Lost in the Queen's maze
6	u_e, ue, oo, ew	c<u>u</u>b<u>e</u>, bl<u>ue</u>, m<u>oo</u>n, f<u>ew</u>, gr<u>ew</u>	Stuck on a dune A day at the zoo The Hat Man's new roof
7	ar, or, er, ir, ur, wr	f<u>ar</u>m, f<u>or</u>, h<u>er</u>, g<u>ir</u>l, f<u>ur</u>, <u>wr</u>ite	The big match Snapshots The bird girls My very bad morning
8	o, oo, u, oy, oi	s<u>o</u>n, b<u>oo</u>k, p<u>u</u>t, b<u>oy</u>, c<u>oi</u>n	Oscar's brother The big pull Nick's noisy new toy
9	aw, au, ow, ou	s<u>aw</u>, c<u>au</u>se, h<u>ow</u>, <u>ou</u>t,	Draw it! The house mouse Look now!
10	Review ear, air	p<u>ear</u>, y<u>ear</u>, f<u>air</u>	My shark dream A fresh feast Bears at the fair A fairy story

Collect the sets

Phonics Readers - Red Series

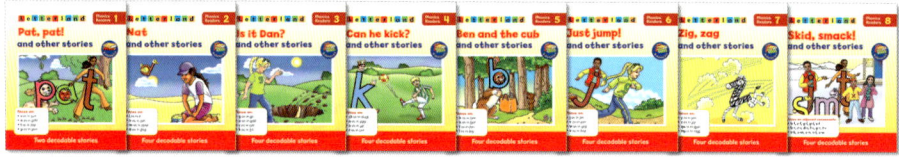

Phonics Readers - Blue Series

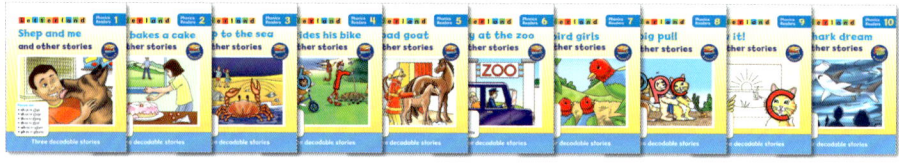

Published by Letterland International Ltd. 8/10 South Street, Epsom, Surrey, KT18 7PF, UK.
www.letterland.com
ISBN: 978-1-78248-184-3
Product Code: TJ06

© Letterland International 2016
LETTERLAND™ is a trademark of Letterland International Ltd.

First published 2013. This new edition published 2016.
Reprinted 2023.
10 9 8 7 6 5 4 3 2

Authors: Stamey Carter and Lisa Holt
Originator of Letterland: Lyn Wendon
Artwork: Doreen Shaw
Design: Lisa Holt

The author asserts the moral right to be identified as the author of this work. All rights reserved. No part of this publication may be reproduced, stored in a retrieval system, or transmitted in any form or by any means, electronic, mechanical, photocopying, recording or otherwise, without either the prior permission of the Publisher or a licence permitting restricted copying in the United Kingdom issued by the Copyright Licensing Agency Ltd, 90 Tottenham Court Road, London W1T 4LP. This book is sold subject to the condition that it shall not be by way of trade or otherwise be lent, hired out or otherwise circulated without the Publisher's prior consent.

Printed in Beirut, Lebanon.